Science Project Guide

Science in Action

Sixth Edition

Project Planning •
Investigation •
Fair Exhibit •
Oral Presentation •

A Beka Book ® Pensacola, FL 32523-9100
an affiliate of PENSACOLA CHRISTIAN COLLEGE®

Science in Action: Science Project Guide
Sixth Edition

Staff Credits
Contributors: Colette Stancel; James Ridgley, Ed.S.; Rick Enders, Ed.S.
Editor: Corinne Sawtelle
Designer: John Halbach

Copyright © mmxii, mcmxcviii, mcmxc, mcmlxxxiii, mcmlxxvii, mcmlxxv
Pensacola Christian College
All rights reserved. Printed in U.S.A. 2014

A Beka Book, a Christian textbook ministry affiliated with Pensacola Christian College, is designed to meet the need for Christian textbooks and teaching aids. The purpose of this publishing ministry is to help Christian schools reach children and young people for the Lord and train them in the Christian way of life.

Photo credit: iStockphoto.com / iLexx (swirls / spheres)

Cataloging Data
　　　　Science in action: science project guide —6th edition.
　　x, 93 p. : ill. ; 28 cm
　　　1. Science—Study and teaching (Secondary). 2. Science projects.
III. A Beka Book, Inc.

Library of Congress: Q180.2 .S25 2011
Dewey System: 507.8

Contents

3 Reporting Your Data 53

4 Preparing Your Exhibit 73

Appendix 77

Introduction

Science in Action is designed to help students complete successful science projects. This work-text contains step-by-step instructions for each stage of the project and includes worksheets, samples, and grading forms.

To begin their projects, students will choose a topic and complete a short background report on it. Next, they will select a specific problem to investigate, plan and conduct the investigation (experiments), and write a followup report summarizing their investigation. The final stage of the project involves the preparation of an exhibit and an oral presentation of the project. Selected projects from each class may be exhibited in a school science fair.

The key to successful science projects is an enthusiastic teacher who encourages his students to prepare outstanding projects by thoroughly teaching the material in this book.

Using *Science in Action*

Scheduling

Your first step will be to fill in the due dates for the Science Project Work Schedule (pp. 3–4). Use your school calendar, your science curriculum, and the Suggested Project Overview (pp. viii–ix). The Work Schedule dates should be given to students at the time the science project is introduced. You may need to extend or shorten deadlines.

Students begin the Science Project by researching background information on the topic they have chosen. This is followed by conducting a scientific investigation, constructing an exhibit, and giving an oral presentation. Students will follow these steps in completing the project:

Step 1 Choose a Project Topic.

    2 Write a Background Paper.

    3 Choose a Problem to Investigate.

    4 Write an Investigation Plan.

    5 Conduct the Investigation.

    6 Write a Followup.

    7 Prepare a Science Project Exhibit.

    8 Give an Oral Presentation.

Students will keep their written reports, Journal, and important forms in a Science Project Notebook. Your regular science class should continue throughout the course of the science project. Some class time may be set aside for students to work on their projects, but as a rule, projects are completed outside the classroom. Oral presentations will need to be scheduled into your daily plans early in second semester (approximately three presentations each day). Science project work should be assigned along with regular homework. Complete science curriculums available from *A Beka Book* already include science project assignments and procedures in the daily plans.

Written Report

The written reports—Background, Investigation Plan, and Followup—may be either handwritten or typed, but all three should be done the same way. Emphasize the information on plagiarism (p. 14). It is important that students understand what plagiarism is and know how to avoid it before they begin writing the Background report. Samples are included for the Background, Investigation Plan, and Followup sections. Students should refer to these samples frequently.

The Presentation/Exhibit

The oral presentation, which includes the exhibit, provides each student with an opportunity to summarize his research. The exhibit is a visual display of the student's work and shows an overview of his entire project. Soon after your last oral presentation, have a school science fair where some or all of your students can exhibit their projects.

If your school intends to send students to a regional science fair, you will want to plan your school science fair to be held prior to the regional fair. Regional science fairs frequently present opportunities for students to discuss their projects with professional scientists who have judged their projects. The judges often will give advice on how to continue the investigation with suggestions for additional work in the specific areas in which your students are interested. Obtain the regional science fair rules early in the fall and acquaint yourself with current requirements.

Science in Action generally conforms to the rules set up by the International Science and Engineering Fair (ISEF). ISEF rules require that advance certification forms be prepared for all types of experiments (additional certification is required for those involving humans or vertebrate animals) *before* beginning the experiment if the project is to be entered in a regional science fair affiliated with ISEF. Refer to current ISEF rules for explanation of certifications and for copies of certifications. Because ISEF rules are frequently modified, the ISEF requirements for the display may differ from the instructions in *Science in Action*, but the information required for the display should be the same. To obtain a copy of current ISEF rules, write to:

Science Service, Inc.
1719 N Street NW
Washington, D.C. 20036

Schedule, Worksheets, Grading Forms

The forms listed below can be used to help you and your students evaluate their work. These forms are located throughout this book.

Science Project Work Schedule
(Students fill in dates and keep at front of Science Project Notebook.)

Worksheets/Evaluation Forms
(for student use)

Topic Selection Worksheet

Problem Selection Worksheet

Getting Started Worksheet

Investigation Plan Self-Evaluation

Grading/Evaluation Forms
(for teacher use)

Background Grade Form

Investigation Plan Evaluations (1st/Revised drafts)

Investigation Plan Grade Form

Followup Grade Form

Final Grade Form (used to grade experimental design/oral presentation/exhibit)

Grading the Exhibit and Oral Presentation

While the student is giving his oral presentation and displaying his exhibit, you will be evaluating the exhibit and the presentation (grade forms in Appendix). At the same time, you will need to decide if the project is eligible for your school's science fair. If possible, check the exhibit more thoroughly before or after class.

See page 76 for a suggested time allotment for the oral presentation by grade. The time allowed for questioning by the audience is not counted as part of the time requirement. Have a student use a stopwatch to time all presentations.

Note: The *A Beka Book* curriculum does not include the experiment and oral presentation for 7th grade or any science project work for 12th grade; however, students in those grades may be assigned projects at your discretion.

Above average projects may be saved and used as aids in instructing your students in the future.

Determining the Grade

The science project is spread over twenty weeks. The following grading guidelines are suggested:

- Count the Background paper (one quiz) and the Investigation Plan (two quizzes) as second quarter grades.

- In the third quarter, grade the Followup as one quiz grade. The Final Grade Form is used on the day of the Oral Presentation to grade the presentation as well as the Exhibit and the Experimental Design of the project. The Final Grade Form counts as one test grade.

Suggested grading forms for each part of the project are included in the Appendix as guidelines for your grading. Adjust the grade distribution and scale as needed to fit your grade level or particular class situation.

Suggested Project Overview

This project overview is based on a typical thirty-six-week school year. Project work starts the third week so that students may become established in academic routines.

Week of School	Introduce/Assign	Items Due	Worksheet or Checklist
3rd week	Introduce Science Project and Science Project Notebook		
5th week	Introduce Background paper (1st draft)	Topic Chosen	Topic Selection Worksheet
6th week	Introduce Investigation Plan and Problem Selection	First Draft of Background paper	
7th week	Explain Investigation Plan (1st draft)	Final Draft of Background paper Chosen Problem or Question	Problem Selection Worksheet
10th week	Explain Revised draft of Investigation Plan	First Draft of Investigation Plan	Investigation Plan Evaluation (1st draft)
11th week	Explain Final Draft of Investigation Plan	Revised Draft of Investigation Plan	Investigation Plan Evaluation (Revised draft)
12th week	Introduce Journal and Assign Getting Started Worksheet	Final Investigation Plan Begin Investigation and Journal	Investigation Plan Grade Form Getting Started Worksheet
13th week		First Journal Check (3 entries)	
14th week		Second Journal Check (6 cumulative entries) Sign up for Oral Presentations (to begin in wk. 21)	

Week of School	Introduce / Assign	Items Due	Worksheet or Checklist
15th week		Third Journal Check (9 cumulative entries)	
16th week	Introduce Exhibit		
17th week	Explain How to Complete Investigation Introduce Investigation Followup	Fourth Journal Check (12 cumulative entries)	
18th week	Explain Details of Exhibit	Fifth Journal Check (15 cumulative entries) Begin Constructing Science Project Exhibit	
19th week		Investigation Complete First Draft of Followup	
20th week	Explain Oral Presentation Remind How to Prepare Science Project Notebook for Exhibit	Final Draft of Followup	Followup Grade Form
21st week		Begin Oral Presentations Science Project Notebook	Oral Presentation / Exhibit Grade Form
22nd week		Continue Oral Presentations	
23rd week		Continue Oral Presentations (if needed)	
24th week	Science Fair	Science Fair	

Chapter 1
Planning Your Project

A science project is a largely independent activity in which you research a topic and then conduct a series of experiments to solve a scientific problem. Science projects give you the opportunity to go beyond what you learn in science class and explore other areas which interest you.

This book is written to guide you in the preparation of a science project. Instructions are given for each part of the project, along with practical suggestions, examples, and ideas.

gluten free cookie different flour brand.

do blonde girls know the back of their hand better the brunettes

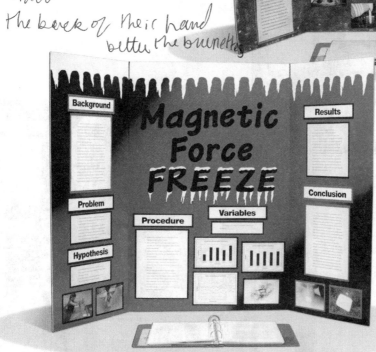

Name _____

Science Project Work Schedule

Fill in the due dates as indicated by your teacher and then remove this schedule and place it in the front of your Science Project Notebook.

Date Due:

(Science Project and Notebook introduced in class)
(First Draft of Background introduced in class)
_____ Choose Topic
      Topic Selection Worksheet Due

_____ First Draft of Background due

(Final Draft of Background introduced in class)
_____ Second Draft of Background Due

_____ Final Draft of Background Due
      (attach Background Grade Form)

(Investigation introduced in class)
_____ Choose Your Problem or Question
      Problem Selection Worksheet Due

_____ First Draft of Investigation Plan Due
      (attach Teacher Investigation Plan Evaluation 1st draft)

_____ Revised Draft Investigation Plan Due
      (attach Teacher Investigation Plan Evaluation Revised draft)

_____ Final Investigation Plan Due
      (attach Investigation Plan Grade Form)

(Journal introduced in class)
_____ Begin Investigation
      Getting Started Worksheet Due

_____ First Journal Check
      (3 entries)

_____ Second Journal Check
      (6 cumulative entries)

_____ Sign up for Oral Presentation

_____ Third Journal Check
      (9 cumulative entries)

(Science Project Exhibit Introduced)
_____ Begin constructing Science Project Exhibit

(Followup explained in class)
_____ Fourth Journal Check
      (12 cumulative entries)

_____ Fifth Journal Check
      (15 cumulative entries)

_____ Investigation complete
      First Draft of Followup Due

(Oral Presentation explained in class)
_____ Final Draft of Followup Due
      (attach Followup Grade Form)

_____ Give Oral Presentation
      (turn in Project Notebook,
      Oral Presentation Grade Form,
      and Exhibit Grade Form)

_____ Science Fair

The first step in beginning a science project is to choose a topic—a field of science you would like to learn more about. Follow the guidelines listed below. Some of the fascinating fields of science you might explore are listed on pages 5–9.

Guidelines for Choosing a Topic

- Choose a specific topic in which you are interested and one with which you are somewhat familiar.
- Choose a topic for which you can find adequate information and which lends itself to safe experimentation.

Sources for Topic Ideas

1. Check science books, encyclopedias, and science project sources.
2. Talk with students who have had successful projects. Also consult with teachers, librarians, and other professionals such as engineers, professors, medical personnel, etc.

Fields of Science

Science can be divided into two general areas—**biological science** (science of living things) and **physical science** (science of nonliving things). Within both of these general areas, there are many specific fields. Each specific field contains many subject areas. The following list will give you ideas of areas from which good science projects could be chosen, although this list is not exhaustive.

Biological Science—the study of living things

Botany—study of plants

- **Agriculture**—science of farming
  (hydroponics, effects of fertilizer, soil pH, amount of water, amount of light, color of light, soil salinity, temperature, etc. on plant growth or seed germination)
- **Forestry**—science of growing trees
  (effects of factors listed under agriculture on germination of tree seeds or growth of very young trees; effects of pruning on tree growth; tree ring studies)

Ecology—study of biotic factors, abiotic factors, carrying capacity, etc. of miniature ecosystems such as flower gardens, ponds, etc.

Microbiology—study of microscopic living things such as bacteria, fungi, molds, protozoa, etc.

(effects of nutrients, salinity, temperature, moisture, lighting [color or intensity], disinfectants, etc. on growth of microorganisms)

Zoology—study of animals

(learning response; intelligence)

- **Entomology**—study of insects
  (effects of factors such as temperature, humidity, light, sound, toxins, abundance of food, etc., or behavior and/or growth of ants, crickets, roaches, or other insects; preferred foods of ants, bees, wasps, roaches, etc.; response of individual insects to various stimuli; visual acuity of insects; insect intelligence; etc.)

- **Invertebrate zoology**—study of coelenterates—hydra, poriferans—sponges, platyhelminths—planaria, annelids—earthworms, arthropods other than insects, etc.
  (effects of factors such as light, temperature, food, etc. on reproduction, behavior and/or regeneration; preferred foods; learning ability)

Physical Science—the study of non-living things

Chemistry—study of composition, structure, and properties of matter

- **Analytical**—study of composition of matter
  (chromatography, qualitative analysis)

- **Inorganic**—study of compounds not containing carbon
  (physical properties of common substances; pH of common substances; construction and testing of electric batteries using various materials; crystals, electrolysis/electroplating)

- **Nuclear**—study of reactions involving the nuclei of atoms
  (radiation shielding)

- **Organic**—study of the composition of carbon compounds
  (production or analysis of soaps and detergents; polymer chemistry; petroleum chemistry)

- **Physical**—study of the physical properties and behaviors of substances
  (diffusion; osmosis; laws of chemical change, conductivity, electrolytes, electrolysis, polymerization)

- **Thermochemistry**—study of heat in relation to chemical reactions
  (heat of solution; exothermic and endothermic reactions; calorimetry; temperature and reaction rates; chemical equilibrium)

Computers and Mathematics

- **Computer Technology**—study of the application of computers to science
  (voice/image recognition; computer simulations of physical processes; robotics/artificial intelligence)

- **Geometry**—mathematical study of shapes
  (examples of geometric patterns in nature [planets = spheres; orbits = ellipses; trajectories = parabolas; fullerenes and intracellular vesicles = geodesic domes; tusks, spiral shells, and spiral galaxies = logarithmic spirals]; properties of shapes in non-Euclidean geometry)

- **Logic**—study of reasoning and deduction
- **Mathematics**—study of applying numeric and symbolic method to real-world phenomena
  (mathematical patterns in nature such as monocot/dicot flower parts and the Golden Spiral; occurrence of in nature [such as in circles, spheres, electrostatic constant, magnetic constant, and certain probability distributions])

Earth Science

- **Astronomy**—study of the stars and other celestial bodies
  (long-term observations of planetary motion, moons of Jupiter, etc.; correlation of lunar phases and height of tides; analysis of space probe data)
- **Conservation**—study of the wise use of natural resources
  (erosion prevention; methods of water desalination; water treatment; energy conservation; pollution control devices)
- **Geology**—study of the earth
  (seismology; volcanology, methods of erosion)
- **Limnology**—study of the geological, physical, biological, and chemical characteristics of inland waters such as lakes, ponds, etc.
- **Meteorology**—study of weather
  (maintain a home weather station and compare accuracy of personal forecasts to professional forecasts; correlation of daily satellite weather photos [available from NOAA on the Internet] with national and regional weather systems and local weather measurements)
- **Mineralogy**—study of minerals
  (physical properties of local rocks and minerals; physical properties of various minerals [hardness, luster, density, etc]; effects of temperature variations, water, acids and bases, etc., on mineral hardness; dripstone formation; comparison of igneous, sedimentary, and metamorphic rocks)
- **Oceanography/Marine Biology**—study of the seas and sea life
  (geology of the coast; beach erosion; sandbar formation; rip current simulation; ocean waves; identification and observation of local marine organisms; chemical analysis of seawater; oceanographic equipment; see also Conservation)
- **Pedology**—study of soil
  (composition and physical properties of different types of local soil; effects of various soil characteristics on plant growth [see Botany]; soil erosion [see Conservation]; identification and observation of soil-dwelling organisms [earthworms, mole crickets, ants, etc.; see also Entomology]; effects of earthworms on soil quality; effects of water, peat, fertilizer, ashes, lime, etc., on soil characteristics [pH, texture, etc.])

Engineering—the application of physics

- **Aerodynamics**—study of gases and solids in relative motion
  (aerodynamic drag of various shapes; laminar and turbulent flow [see also Hydrodynamics]; effects of airfoil shape on aerodynamic lift; the Bernoulli principle; reducing the aerodynamic drag of an automobile or bicycle)

- **Architecture/Civil Engineering**—study and design of buildings and other structures
  (strength of various types of trusses, arches, etc. [tested with models]; strength of various building materials [compression, shear, tension, stress, or strain]; buildings and earthquakes; designing buildings for energy efficiency; dam construction)

- **Communications**—study of information transmission
  (radio, telegraph, telephone, television, microwave)

- **Hydrodynamics**—study of liquids in motion
  (the Bernoulli principle; hydrodynamic drag of various shapes; hydrodynamic drag of various shapes of ships' hulls [tested with models]; hydrofoils; turbulence)

- **Hydrostatics**—study of liquids at rest
  (pressure and depth; pressure and fluid density; effects of various factors on buoyancy [density of fluid, depth, volume of buoyant material]; Archimedes' principle; Pascal's principle; hydraulics)

Physics—study of interaction between matter and energy

- **Electrostatics/Electrodynamics**—study of the behavior of electrons
  (conductivity/resistance of common metals, nonmetals, and electrolytes; conductivity and temperature; resistance heat; electric lighting; types of electric circuits; electric generators [types of generators; factors affecting power production; "alternative" energy sources]; photovoltaic cells; superconductivity [see also Magnetism]; electromagnetic induction [see also Magnetism]; electric motors)

- **Electronics**—study of technology based on electron behavior
  (electronic components; semiconductor devices; electronic circuits [audio oscillators, capacitor discharge circuits, radio receivers, etc.]; oscilloscope studies of oscillators; see also Computer Technology)

- **Magnetism**—study of magnets
  (permanent magnets vs. temporary magnets; electromagnets)

- **Mechanics**—study of motion and forces
  (first law of motion [mass and inertia]; second law of motion [force and acceleration]; third law of motion [action and reaction in static and/or dynamic systems; force pairs]; momentum [calculation of; conservation of in collisions]; kinetic energy [kinetic energy vs. momentum;

kinetic energy transfer]; gravitation [acceleration of gravity; Galileo's falling-body experiments; free fall]; trajectories of projectiles [may be anything from basketballs and baseballs to rifle bullets]; motion dynamics of a trebuchet [could construct softball-throwing model]; rotary motion [centripetal and centrifugal force; Coriolis effect; conservation of angular momentum; flywheels as a means of energy storage; gyroscopic effects])

- **Optics**—study of the behavior of light (reflection; refraction; diffraction; interference; iridescence; perception of color; lasers; holography; photography; reflector shape in directed lighting; telescopes)

- **Thermodynamics**—study of energy and heat transfer (methods of heat transfer; heat transfer in various solids; convection rate in various fluids; color and radiant heat absorption; heat engines; thermal efficiency of engines; harnessing waste heat; latent heat; refrigeration; conservation of mass-energy/first law of thermodynamics; entropy/second law of thermodynamics)

- **Waves and Acoustics**—study of waves and sound (behavior of water waves; speed of sound; behavior of sound waves; harmony and dissonance; oscilloscope studies)

Topic Approval and Project Goals

1. Once you have selected a topic, complete the **Topic Selection Worksheet** on page 11 and submit it to your teacher for approval. Be ready to offer an alternate choice if needed.

2. Purchase a 3-ring binder (approximately 1" size) to use as a **Science Project Notebook.** In this notebook, you will keep all of the written materials for your science project. Since the items in this notebook are irreplaceable, be sure it is clearly identified with your name and keep it in a safe place. It will be part of your Science Project Exhibit.

3. Complete the **Science Project Work Schedule** on pages 3–4 when your teacher gives the dates. Place the Work Schedule in the front of your Science Project Notebook and refer to it often to avoid missing a deadline.

Topic Selection Worksheet

I. The general field of science that I have chosen for my science project topic is:

☐ Biological

☐ Physical

II. The general area of the field I have chosen is:

_____.

III. The specific topic I have chosen is:

_____.

After this topic has been approved, place this worksheet in your Science Project Notebook.

Teacher Response:

☐ Topic approved

☐ Submit a new topic

Guidelines for Writing the Background

▣ What is the Background?

It is a brief overview of essential general information concerning your topic (the specific field of science that you have chosen) followed by a short description of possible investigations that could be done relating to that topic.

When your project and display are complete, the Background will be positioned on the top left corner of the board. It is the first part of the board that is seen. It lays the foundation for everything on the remainder of the board.

▣ What are the purposes of the Background?

It enables you to learn enough about your topic to plan and conduct an effective scientific investigation.

It acquaints those who read your display board with the basic facts of your topic so that they can understand the investigation described on the rest of the display board.

▣ What specifically should I write about in the Background?

The first 2–4 paragraphs should discuss the basic facts of your topic. It should give people a foundational understanding of your topic. In addition, it may inspire someone with ideas for his own scientific investigation.

The last 1–2 paragraphs should briefly describe investigations (experiments) that could be conducted concerning this topic. These paragraphs provide the transition to the remainder of the display (beginning with the Problem) so that when someone reading your display board finishes the Background, there is a smooth transition into the remaining material describing the actual investigation.

▣ What does not need to be included?

Discussion of the broad field(s) that relate to your topic do not need to be included. Stick to the specific, narrow topic that you have chosen.

Specific explanations as to how to conduct investigations are not needed.

▣ What are the specific requirements for the Background?

Length—300–350 words

Typed with 14–18 point type; or handwritten with your best penmanship

If typing, observe a 1-inch margin on all sides.

If handwriting, observe margins and write on the front of the paper only.

Begin with a heading that includes the title of the paper (Background) centered, with your name centered on the next line as shown on p. 17.

◼ Where do I find materials for my report?

1. *Reader's Guide to Periodical Literature:* One fast way to locate magazine articles is to use the *Reader's Guide to Periodical Literature*. This monthly publication catalogs articles (by subject) from a variety of periodicals. Your library may also have a periodical database that you could search.

2. **Catalog:** An index to the entire library book collection is contained in an online catalog or a card catalog. Both catalogs provide information by author, title, and subject. By looking up your topic, you can determine what books are available in a library. After you have determined the general location of library books about your topic, it is often helpful to go to that area and search for other potential sources. You can determine the usefulness of a source by referring to the Table of Contents and/or Index.

3. **Internet services:** Another source of information may be the Internet. If you use the Internet, be sure to record the web address for future reference. Parental supervision is recommended when using the Internet.

◼ How can I avoid plagiarism?

Plagiarism is defined in the *American Heritage College Dictionary* as "**copying** or **imitating** the language, ideas, and thoughts of another author and passing off the same as one's original work."

To avoid plagiarism, reword any published information (even common knowledge, facts, etc.) in *your own words,* with *your own sentence structure.* It is not enough to just change a few words. The material must be completely reworded. The *organization* of the material must also be your own. If you use the author's exact words, they must be enclosed in quotation marks. Quotations, opinions, and little-known facts should always be documented. Well-known facts and common knowledge, however, should not require documentation if the words and organization are your own.

Most of the information in your Background should be established facts and common knowledge; therefore, it should not require any specific documentation in the body of the paper. Avoid direct quotations in your Background by putting all of the information into your own words. If your Background should happen to contain quotations or opinions from a particular author, however, you will need to credit the source with a citation. (For information on formatting of citations, see the Appendix in the back of this book.)

◙ *How many drafts are required?*

You will write a first (rough) draft and a final draft.

◙ *How should I revise the first draft?*

1. Ask yourself the following questions:

   a. Does the paper have *unity?* (Do all parts contribute to the single idea of the whole?)

   b. Does it have *coherence?* (Are the ideas organized so that the thought flows smoothly from beginning to end?)

   c. Does it give an overall background structure to your topic? In other words, is it clear and complete?

2. Have someone read your paper and give his overall impression.

3. Determine what needs to be removed, added, or rearranged.

4. Rewrite the paper until you are confident that you have included the right amount of information and have arranged it in the best order.

◙ *How do I prepare my final draft?*

1. Type your final draft carefully from the revised draft. If you are handwriting the paper, write in blue or black ink.

2. Proofread the final copy and make any needed corrections.

3. Turn in the completed paper and the **Background Grade Form.**

4. After your Background paper is returned, keep it in your Science Project Notebook.

Important Final Reminder—Since the Background lays the foundation for your entire investigation and display board, you'll want to do thorough, accurate research. Seek sources of information that are clear and understandable. Verify the information and explain it simply but accurately. Be specific within your narrow field, and do not stray outside that field. Be so thorough in writing your paper that you can place it "as is" directly onto your display board at the conclusion of your project without making any changes. Of course, it will be allowable to make changes to your Background, but you'll save valuable time if changes are not needed.

Background

By _____ your name

Ants are known as social insects. They live in a community called a colony that may include a dozen to millions of members. Most ant colonies are divided into three groups called castes. These castes include the queen, workers, and males. Even though the queen establishes a colony, she does not rule it. The job of the queen is simply to lay eggs for the rest of her life.

One of the major tasks of the workers is to keep the nest clean. Compared to humans, ants probably keep a cleaner living area than humans do. They do not clean themselves with soap and water like humans do, but they simply lick one another, and they lick the queen to keep her clean. The female worker ants actually run the colony. Some of their responsibilities include caring for the queen, as well as enlarging, repairing, and defending the nest. Workers also care for the young and gather food. Worker ants come in many different sizes. Some workers are very large and have the responsibility of guarding the colony. These workers are called soldiers. They have an especially large head and mandibles to fight off enemies. Because the soldier guards the entrance to the nest, it may

1

block an enemy from entering by blocking the entrance of the
tunnel with its head.

Males have an easy life because they do not work at all.
Their life is short, and their only job in life is to mate with
the queen. Most ants build their colony by digging tunnels
and chambers in the soil. One of the chambers is known as the
queen's chamber because that is where the eggs are laid. Other
chambers are busy places as well because after the eggs are laid,
these eggs quickly change to larva and pupa and have to be cared
for in special chambers. In some other chambers, workers rest
for a time after all the hard work that they put in. Some nests
may be as small as your finger and some may extend as long as
forty feet underground. More than ten million ants may live in
a nest. It is possible to study a colony of ants as they work
and eat in a plastic container called an ant farm. Most farms
will only last a few weeks if they do not have a queen. Some
of the different kinds of ants that could be observed in an ant
farm are fire, harvester, honey, and carpenter ants.

An interesting investigation involving ants would be to
compare the speed at which different species of ants form
tunnels and chambers as well as the length of the tunnel
systems. One may also be interested in what type of food is

3

preferred by various ant species. It would also be interesting

to see how long a colony can survive without a queen.

Chapter 2

Experimentation

Now that you have chosen a science project topic and have written a Background paper, it is time for you to exercise your creativity to plan a scientific investigation. *A **scientific investigation** is an extended experiment or series of experiments designed to provide the answer to a scientific problem or question.*

Investigation Plan

The first step in planning a scientific investigation is to think of a scientific problem you would like to solve or a question you would like to answer. On the following pages, example investigations from several major fields of science are described. These examples will give you an idea of the kinds of scientific investigations you can do.

Sample Problems

Zoology:

An interesting question you can answer about bees would be, "Do bees have a color preference?" Place colored paper (red, yellow, blue) with a container of sugar water on it in an area near a beehive. Use a piece of black paper with a container of sugar water on it for the control. Count the number of bees that are attracted to each color.

Chemistry:

You might enjoy tackling this problem: "Can drinking water be obtained from seawater?" Research biological and mechanical osmosis. Experiment with various semipermeable membranes. Try to develop a practical apparatus to desalinate seawater.

A very practical question you can answer is, "Which brand of spray paint best resists visible wear?" Spray various brands of paint on several paint sticks. Allow the paint to dry, and then test the paint for resistance to fading, scratching, cracking, water wear, and chemical wear.

Physics:

Here is a question you can answer with household materials: "Which household container is the best insulator?" Use thermos bottles, glass bottles, plastic bottles, and other bottles to find which bottles best keep cold liquids cold and hot liquids hot.

Meteorology:

You can answer the question, "Is it possible for an amateur to make accurate weather forecasts?" Use weather instruments made from household materials to measure air pressure, humidity, temperature, and other factors each day. Predict the weather for the next day with these measurements and calculate accuracy. Compare the accuracy of personal forecasts to those available in newspapers, television, and radio.

Engineering:

a. If you like to build, you could answer the question, "Which truss design provides the most strength in bridge construction and home construction?" Show how different truss designs affect the strength of bridges and other structures.

b. You could answer the question, "How do different tread designs and tread materials perform on different surfaces?" Prepare simulated road surfaces (concrete block, brick, asphalt, and others). Test various combinations to see which one results in the best grip (the most friction) on each surface.

Note: The above investigation involves three different experiments (tread designs, tread materials, and three different surfaces). Excellent investigations often include several experiments.

Botany:

If you enjoy growing plants, you could answer the question, "What factors affect the growth of a hydroponic garden?" Grow strawberries, lettuce, and/or beans in a hydroponic garden. Determine the effect of different gravel sizes, water flow rates, lighting, and fertilizers on plant growth rate.

Sources for Problems to Investigate

1. Check science textbooks and science project idea books.

2. Talk with students who have had successful projects.

3. Ask advice from professionals such as teachers, librarians, engineers, college professors, medical personnel, etc.

4. With your teacher's permission, you may continue an investigation as long as you have new aspects of the problem to explore and will not be repeating work you have already done.

Guidelines for Choosing a Problem

◼ What should I consider in choosing a problem or question to answer?

Choose a problem...

1. that you can solve by making careful observations and doing experiments that will produce measurable results.

   Example: Tooth investigations (decay, whiteness) should usually be avoided because the results are very difficult to measure.

2. that is specific, testing only one factor (variable) per experiment.

   Example: An investigation to determine the effect of nitrogen and potassium on rye grass and corn plants would be improved by narrowing its focus to one nutrient tested on one type of plant.

3. that is within your ability to accomplish considering the time, equipment, and know-how available to you and that will not be hindered by geographic location or adverse weather conditions.

   Examples:

   Time—because plant grafting requires several months, it may not be a workable problem to investigate.

   Equipment—because studying protozoa requires a microscope, it would not be a good choice for those who do not have access to a microscope.

   Weather—because plant growth projects such as fertilizer effectiveness require warm weather and sunshine, they may not be practical during certain seasons of the year.

   Geographic location—because the study of minerals requires analyzing local rocks, it is an impractical choice for those who live in areas where rocks are difficult to obtain.

4. for which test subjects are available and will not be harmed by the experimentation.

   Examples:

   Humans—because experiments involving human exercise could be harmful to those involved, this area should usually be avoided.

   Note: Many experiments involving humans are impractical due to the difficulty of finding a sufficient number of people (at least twenty-five) available to participate.

   Animals—because depriving a mouse of essential nutrients could be harmful, this topic should be avoided.

5. that has a practical application.

   Example: An intriguing question such as, "Can plants thrive on milk since mammals thrive on it?" is not the source of a good investigation since it is outside the realm of standard plant growth technique and therefore, has no real-life use.

   It is often necessary to consider more than one problem before finding one that is interesting and workable. As you think of possible problems or questions, use the Problem Selection Worksheet (p. 27) to assist you. Submit your completed Problem Selection Worksheet to your teacher for approval on the date indicated on the Science Project Work Schedule. Place the approved worksheet in your Science Project Notebook.

◼ What should I avoid in choosing a problem to investigate?

1. Avoid investigations dealing with vertebrate animals. If you have a definite experiment in mind concerning an animal with a backbone, check with your teacher for the requirements involved.

2. Avoid making a model or doing a demonstration and calling it an investigation.

3. Avoid investigations that can be completed in a few days. A good investigation will be a **long-term** undertaking involving an extended experiment or a series of several related experiments.

Safety Concerns

Safety is a major concern in planning an investigation. Carefully read the following special concerns.

Chemicals: Be careful when working with any chemicals, including household ones. Read the directions for safe handling and disposal. Be careful in the handling of substances like nail polish remover (acetone), rubbing alcohol, fertilizers, plant foods, and vitamins. Adult supervision is recommended.

Equipment: Your parents need to be aware of equipment you plan to use. Use of equipment such as knives, blenders, and power tools should be supervised at home.

Bacteria: If you are planning to grow bacteria or fungi, you should order kits from science supply catalogs and use aseptic technique to grow a known strain of bacteria. Collecting bacteria or fungi from the air, from a surface, or from a person's mouth is unacceptable.

Electricity: Adult supervision is required for the use of AC or DC over 12 volts. No open-top cells are allowed. As a rule, use direct current (from batteries) rather than alternating current. Insulate all exposed wiring.

People: Projects involving humans require special handling. Survey questions of a personal nature are unacceptable. All test results should be anonymous. Avoid any project posing a risk to the subjects. Projects with acceptable risk, such as healthy people exercising, will need to be supervised by a qualified adult, such as an exercise instructor or health care professional.

ISEF (International Science and Engineering Fair) rules ban *all* experiments on minors (even surveys) unless there is prior review of procedure and written parental consent of *each* minor being tested—refer to latest ISEF rules for clarification. (ISEF bans surveys on minors because federal law bans them unless parental consent is given.) It is best to obtain written permission of the people involved for *any* investigation concerning humans, regardless of age.

Vertebrate animals: Since many laws regulate experimentation with animals, vertebrate animal projects are difficult to carry out. It is wiser to use invertebrate animals unless your problem involves observing animals in their natural habitat.

Firearms, fire, or explosives: Projects involving firearms, fire, or explosives are generally prohibited. However, with parental permission and supervision, some projects involving fire or firearms might be acceptable.

Name _____   Due _____

Problem Selection Worksheet

I. The general field of science that I have chosen for my science project topic is:

☐ Biological

☐ Physical

The specific area of the field I have chosen is:

_____.

(Refer to your Topic Selection Worksheet if necessary.)

II. State the problem(s) you would like to solve or the question(s) you would like to answer.

III. To help you to develop a workable procedure, answer the following questions:
(Refer to Guidelines for Writing an Investigation Plan.)

A. Will you be comparing two or more things? If so, what are they?

B. What will your variable be?

C. How will you measure the result? (length, time, weight, etc.)

IV. Supplies

    A. List the five most important items you might need to conduct this investigation.

        1.

        2.

        3.

        4.

        5.

    B. Where will you get these supplies?

    C. If you have to buy supplies, about how much will they cost? Is this amount affordable?

V. Will you be able to conduct this investigation at home, or will you need to do it in a laboratory?

VI. Will geographic location or environmental conditions such as weather (cloudy days, cold days, or rainy days), length of days, etc., affect your ability to conduct this investigation?

VII. Will you be able to complete this investigation in the time available as indicated by the Science Project Work Schedule?

VIII. Do your parents approve of this investigation idea?

Guidelines for Writing an Investigation Plan

Once you have decided on a problem or question, the next step is to design the investigation. Remember, a scientific investigation is *an extended experiment or series of experiments designed to provide the answer to a scientific problem or question.* The characteristics of a good scientific investigation can be summarized as follows:

A good investigation...

1. should be as **specific** as possible.

   Example: Rather than testing the effects of nutrients on plants, test one specific nutrient such as nitrogen or potassium, on one specific type of plant such as radishes.

2. should be designed so that the results of the experiment are observable as well as being **measurable** or **countable.**

   Example: In the fertilizer example mentioned above, the results were obtained by observing the plants as well as measuring the height of each plant and counting the number of leaves per plant twice each week.

3. should have one or more **experimental groups**.

   Example: The fertilizer example used three groups of plants to determine how nitrogen fertilizers affected plant growth. The group(s) on which the experiment will be performed are called experimental group(s).

4. should have only **one variable. All other factors will be held constant.**

   Example: Among the three groups of plants used in the fertilizer investigation, all factors were held constant (type of soil, type of plants used, the number of seeds per cup, amount of sunlight, amount of water, age of plants when fertilizer was first applied, and the frequency of watering and fertilizing)

except the nitrogen content of the fertilizer, which was the variable.

5. may have a **control.** The control proves that the factor being tested actually caused the observed result. It is a basis for comparison, the one logical explanation for the results that occur. Investigations in which test subjects are compared to each other may not need a control.

   Example: In the fertilizer investigation, the control was a group of plants to which no fertilizer was added. This group showed how plants of this type grew without nitrogen fertilizer. When the other groups of plants showed variations from the control group, the logical explanation for these variations was that they were caused by the differing amounts of nitrogen applied.

6. should be **extensive;** it should be carried out for a period of time (days or weeks) and should test a large population.

   Example: The fertilizer investigation used 90 plants (2 groups of 30 plants each, plus a control group of 30 plants). The plants were observed for 8 weeks.

7. should have a **large sample size** or be **repeated** several times for accuracy. Both criteria may apply to some projects. Each repetition is called a trial.

8. may have results that you **compare to known data.**

   Example: One student made his own hydrometer and used it to test the specific gravity of 20 substances. He compared his results to the known specific gravity of each substance. Another student made her own calorimeter. She used it to determine the calorie content per gram of several foods and compared her results to the known calorie content of each of the foods.

Questions to Consider When Writing the Investigation Plan

As you plan your investigation, you will need to answer the following questions:

1. Do the steps I need to follow comprise a single experiment or several experiments?

2. What will I measure or count to determine the result of my experiment(s)?

3. What is the experimental group for each of the experiments and how many subjects will it contain?

4. What is the control group (if needed) for each experiment and how many subjects will it contain?

5. What are the constant factors for each experiment?

6. What is the variable for each experiment?

7. Will I need to repeat my experiments to get accurate results? If so, how many times?

8. How will I graph the results? What data will be plotted on each axis?

9. Is known data available for comparison with my results? If so, where will I get this data?

10. What safety procedures will I need to follow?

Steps in Writing the Investigation Plan

Step 1: Write your first draft. Include these sections:

1. **Problem**—the question you intend to answer

2. **Hypothesis**—the expected solution to your question/problem

3. **Procedure**—a step-by-step description of the method you will use to answer your question or solve your problem. Also, state the materials that you will use. (If you use a procedure from a published source instead of one you devised yourself, credit the source.)

4. **Conclusion**—a standard which allows you to decide whether your hypothesis proves true or not. The standard would be a specific measurement change (Ex: If the height of the plants increases by at least 5 cm, I will conclude that my hypothesis is correct). It is often necessary to do research to effectively set a standard.

5. **Safety**—an explanation of safety procedures that you will follow

Step 2: Revise your first draft. The purpose of this revised plan is to make any changes (restrictions, safety precautions, etc.) your teacher has suggested. After your teacher checks your revised copy, do any final editing needed.

Step 3: Prepare your final copy. Follow the Investigation Plan Self-Evaluation. Include a title page. You will not have an outline, and you will not need a bibliography entry unless you used a procedure from a published source. Remember to use the headings, format, and spacing illustrated in the sample Investigation Plan. Submit the Investigation Plan Grade Form with your Investigation Plan.

Teacher should collect, grade, and return papers.

Note: Place your graded Investigation Plan in your Science Project Notebook. This plan will be your guide as you conduct your investigation.

Investigation Plan Self-Evaluation

Use the following questions to help you improve your Investigation Plan:

Problem

Is it specific?

Weak: Which detergent is best?

Better: Among Brand A, Brand B, and Brand C, which is most effective at removing grape juice and mustard stains from cotton cloth?

Did you state a separate problem for each experiment?

Hypothesis

Did you give a reason for your hypothesis?

Did you state a separate hypothesis for each experiment?

Procedure

Have you clearly stated all of the items below for **each** experiment?

- Experimental group
- Control
- Number of items in experimental group
- Variable
- Constant factors
- Number of trials
- Types of measurements (lengths, weights, times, etc.)
- Tools, instruments, and units of measure you will use
- Method of graphing results including the type of data to be plotted on each axis
- Types of observations you will record

Did you state the number of experiments you will have?

Have you used metric measuring units?

Conclusion Section

Did you state the change in data that is needed to verify the hypothesis for each experiment?

Safety

Have you thought through your procedure for potential safety issues? Are your safety procedures pertinent to your experiment?

2 inches

INVESTIGATION PLAN

YOUR NAME
DATE
TEACHER'S NAME
CLASS

2 inches

INVESTIGATION PLAN

PROBLEM

Do Western harvester ants dig tunnels at a different rate
when in an artificial environment made of gel compared to the
same ants in their natural habitat? A second question is, "Is
the width of the tunnels of Western harvester ants affected
when they are placed in an artificial habitat compared to their
natural habitat?"

HYPOTHESIS

My hypothesis is that ants will not tunnel in the artificial
environment as quickly as when they are in a natural habitat
such as sand or soil because God designed them specifically
to dig in the natural habitat that He placed them in. A
second hypothesis is that the width of the tunnels will not
be affected whether the ants are tunneling in gel or in soil
because they always need the same width of tunnel to be able
to move efficiently, no matter what material they are tunneling
through.

PROCEDURE

To begin this experiment, I will purchase two ant farms
(formicariums) from a science supply company. One will be an

1

empty ant farm, and the other will be filled with a special gel.
The dimensions of both formicariums will be 16.5 centimeters
in length, 2.5 centimeters in width, and 7.5 centimeters in
depth. I will fill the empty formicarium with sandy soil (the
natural habitat of the ants). Finally, I will purchase apples
to use as food and obtain an eyedropper to give water to the
ants. I will give them 50 milligrams of apple every two days
and 5 milliliters of water every day.

I will also order Western harvester ants; their scientific
name is *Pogonomyrmex occidentalis.* These ants have a nasty
sting so I will have to handle them with forceps. In order to
transfer them from the shipping container to both formicariums,
I will place the shipping container in the refrigerator for ten
minutes until the ants slow down enough so that I can transfer
them safely. During the first transfer, I will place fifteen
ants in the formicarium with the gel and close the lid. Then
I will transfer fifteen more ants to the formicarium with the
sandy soil. It is normal for the ants to take several days to
get used to their environment before they start to tunnel. I
will observe the ants every eight hours to see if they have
begun to tunnel. I will measure the length of the tunnels in
millimeters or centimeters depending on how far they tunnel

3

and will mark the spot where tunneling stopped by securing a

detachable adhesive note to the outside of the formicarium.

There is no control group in my experiment because I am

simply comparing two different habitats to each other. The

variable in my investigation will be the two different habitats

(formicariums). The constant factors will be the type of ants,

the location of the formicariums, the amount of food I give to

each group, and the temperature and lighting of the room. I

will make four starter holes in the gel and in the sandy soil

immediately after introducing the ants by using a small dowel

or peg so that I am sure that the diameter of each hole is the

same. I will make two holes 1 centimeter deep and the other two

2.5 centimeters deep. I will initially add fifteen ants to each

formicarium and increase the number to twenty-five after two

hours.

Every eight hours, I will take measurements of the increase

in tunnel length, diameter of the tunnels, and the number of

ants that were digging at one time. At the same time that I

record measurements, I will also record observations of the

activity level and behavior (aggressive, calm, etc.) of the

ants. I will take readings and make observations for twenty-one

days.

4

After each daily measurement, I will record the cumulative total tunnel length and make a line graph of the results. I will then determine the average number of centimeters that the ants tunneled each hour and make a bar graph of the results. The line graph will display the cumulative daily totals for tunnel length. The x-axis will be the number of days, and the y-axis will be the cumulative distance tunneled in centimeters. One of the bar graphs will display the daily tunnel growth over the twenty-one-day period with the x-axis as the variable (gel versus soil) and the y-axis as the distance tunneled in centimeters. The other bar graphs will display the average hourly and daily tunnel growth.

CONCLUSION

If the rate per hour, per day, and the average rate of tunneling that the Western harvester ants tunnel in the natural habitat is greater than 2 centimeters more when compared to those ants that tunnel in the artificial gel, then it would be correct to conclude that my hypothesis is true. If the width of the tunnels in the artificial gel is at least 2 millimeters different from that of the width of the tunnels of the natural habitat, then my second hypothesis would also be true.

5

SAFETY

(1) I will use goggles and gloves when handling the ants.

(2) I will have adult supervision when working with the ants.

(3) I will carefully read the directions regarding using the gel and ants together.

Name _____   Due _____

Answer the following questions to evaluate your planning as you begin your investigation. After your teacher returns this worksheet, place it in your Science Project Notebook. If a question does not apply to your investigation, write NA (not applicable) to the left of the question.

Answer by circling Y (yes) or N (no).

Y   N   1. Have you placed all previously completed worksheets in your notebook?

Y   N   2. Do you currently have all the equipment and supplies you will need to complete your investigation?

Y   N   3. Have you called local stores to check on the availability of equipment and supplies you still need to purchase?

Y   N   4. Have you placed an order for equipment and supplies that are not available locally?

Y   N   5. Have you made arrangements to get technical help from professionals if needed?

Y   N   6. Have you made arrangements to use a laboratory if needed?

Y   N   7. Have you made any entries in your journal? (The gathering and purchasing of materials should be entered into your journal.)

Y   N   8. Have you arranged to handle all safety concerns mentioned in your Investigation Plan?

Y   N   9. Is there any part of your procedure that you are still uncertain about how to accomplish? If so, please list below:

As you conduct your investigation, keep complete and accurate records of your work in a journal. Plan to keep your journal in your Science Project Notebook. Make a journal entry every time you work on your project. Think of the journal as the "diary" of your investigation.

Guidelines for Writing a Journal

◙ *What format should I use when writing my journal?*

1. Refer to the Sample Journal on p. 49 for correct format.

2. Keep your journal entries as neat as possible. You may have to cross through data or make changes as you conduct your investigation, but it is not necessary to rewrite a page unless it is illegible.

3. It is fine to make a simple list of data, but it is usually better to organize it into a chart. Charts should also be used to organize averages and other calculations for easy reference. When making a chart, remember the following:

   a. Use a ruler to neatly draw the chart right in your journal.

   b. Draw as many columns as you need.

   c. Label each column and give the chart a title.

Here is an example of how you could organize your first five measurements of the length of ant tunnels into easy-to-read chart form.

Ant Tunnel Growth in Length for First Five Days (cm)—November 16					
Natural Habitat (soil)			Artificial Habitat (gel)		
Day Number	Daily Growth of Tunnel (cm)	Cumulative Total Tunnel Length (cm)	Day Number	Daily Growth of Tunnel (cm)	Cumulative Total Tunnel Length (cm)
1	2.5	2.5	1	1.8	1.8
2	3.0	5.5	2	2.5	4.3
3	3.5	9.0	3	2.5	6.8
4	3.7	12.7	4	3.0	9.8
5	4.5	17.2	5	3.1	12.9
Total = 17.2 cm			Total = 12.9 cm		
Avg. Length = 3.4 cm			Avg. Length = 2.6 cm		

◙ *What should I include in my journal?*

1. Include a detailed description of the work you do, (including the equipment and techniques you use), the problems you encountered, and the solutions you find for the problems. Sketches showing how you set up your equipment can also be helpful.

2. Include a record and analysis of the data. The data consists of the actual numbers and measurements you obtain. Use metric units for all measurements. Write down *all* data even if you think something is not significant. Your analysis includes all calculations you do with the data, such as averaging, inserting the numbers into formulas, etc. These are the calculations that enable you to arrive at a final conclusion.

3. Include a description of observations you make while doing the work.

◙ *When will my journal be due?*

Your teacher will check your journal periodically to monitor progress on your investigation. Your complete journal (minimum of 20 entries) will be due at the end of the project as part of your Science Project Notebook.

DATE: November 10

TIME: 5:25–6:00 p.m.

ENTRY NUMBER	1
TOTAL MINUTES THIS ENTRY	35
CUMULATIVE TOTAL MINUTES TO DATE	35

WORK: I gathered the materials for my investigation. I purchased the following:
Formicarium with sand and colony of Western harvester ants—$25.00
Formicarium with gel and colony of Western harvester ants—$30.00
Clear metric ruler—$1.50

OBSERVATION/DATA:

DATE: November 11

TIME: 4:00–5:15 p.m.

WORK: I set up my experiment by following this procedure:

1. I placed the two formicariums in my laundry room so that they will be in the same temperature.

2. One formicarium was already filled with gel; the other I filled with an equal volume of soil.

3. I placed the shipping container with the ants in the refrigerator for ten minutes to slow down their movement so that I could easily transfer them to the formicariums.

4. With the forceps and gloves, I placed fifteen ants into the gel formicarium then closed the top. I then repeated the same procedure with the formicarium with soil.

5. I made four starter holes in the gel and in the soil using a golf tee to make sure the diameter of each hole was the same. Two holes were 1 cm deep and the other two were 2.5 cm deep.

6. I fed the ants by placing 50 mg of apple and 5 mL of water in each formicarium. I will continue supplying the apple every two days and the water each day.

OBSERVATION/DATA: I noticed the ants were very active once they had entered the formicarium; after one hour most began to slow down. After eight hours, I noticed that three or four began to dig a tunnel.

DATE: November 16

TIME: 7:00–7:15 p.m.

ENTRY NUMBER   11

TOTAL MINUTES
THIS ENTRY   15

CUMULATIVE TOTAL
MINUTES TO DATE   245

WORK:

1. I fed and watered the ants with the apple and water.

2. I observed the behavior of the ants and measured the tunnels.

3. I made a table to summarize the data collected for the first five days.

OBSERVATION / DATA:

Today is day five of observing the ant formicariums. The ants in the soil were working on one tunnel with an evening measurement of 2.5 cm. Taking that measurement and adding that to the morning measurement, I obtained the total length of tunneling for the day (4.5 cm).

The ants in the gel had produced three tunnels with an increase of 2.0 cm beyond the morning measurement, which was 1.1 cm. I added these two numbers to obtain the total length of tunneling for the day (3.1 cm).

Ant Tunnel Increase in Length for First Five Days (cm) — November 16

Natural Habitat (soil)			Artificial Habitat (gel)		
Day Number	Daily Growth of Tunnel (cm)	Cumulative Total Tunnel Length (cm)	Day Number	Daily Growth of Tunnel (cm)	Cumulative Total Tunnel Length (cm)
1	2.5	2.5	1	1.8	1.8
2	3.0	5.5	2	2.5	4.3
3	3.5	9.0	3	2.5	6.8
4	3.7	12.7	4	3.0	9.8
5	4.5	17.2	5	3.1	12.9
Total = **17.2 cm** Avg. Length = **3.4 cm**			Total = **12.9 cm** Avg. Length = **2.6 cm**		

DATE: December 18

TIME: 6:00–7:15 p.m.

ENTRY NUMBER _____32_____

TOTAL MINUTES
THIS ENTRY _____75_____

CUMULATIVE TOTAL
MINUTES TO DATE _____950_____

WORK:

1. In a calculation spreadsheet, I set up a formula to figure the average hourly and daily tunneling length in centimeters for the ants in both the gel and the soil.

2. After I calculated the average hourly and daily tunneling length for both groups, I calculated the difference in centimeters of how much greater the ants in the soil tunneled per hour and per day than the ants in the gel.

3. I also calculated the cumulative tunnel growth for both groups of ants.

4. I determined that there was no difference in tunnel width between the two groups.

OBSERVATION/DATA:

The chart below is the data for the daily tunnel growth by day for both groups including the daily and hourly averages. I graphed this data and included in the followup.

Day	1	2	3	4	5	6	7	8	9	10	11	12
Gel	1.8	2.5	2.5	3.0	3.1	3.4	4.0	4.3	4.5	4.5	4.8	4.6
Soil	2.5	3.0	3.5	3.7	4.5	4.8	5.4	5.8	6.3	6.5	6.5	7.0

Day	13	14	15	16	17	18	19	20	21	Tot.	Day	Hr.
Gel	5.5	5.8	6.5	6.8	6.6	7.3	7.8	7.4	7.6	104.1	5.0	0.2
Soil	6.8	7.4	7.8	8.0	8.3	7.9	8.8	8.4	8.5	131.4	6.3	0.3

The chart below is the cumulative tunnel growth by day for both groups. I graphed this data and included in the followup.

Day	1	2	3	4	5	6	7	8	9	10	11
Gel	1.8	4.3	6.8	9.8	12.9	16.3	20.3	24.6	29.1	33.6	38.3
Soil	2.5	5.5	9.0	12.7	17.2	22.0	27.4	33.2	39.5	46.0	52.5

Day	12	13	14	15	16	17	18	19	20	21
Gel	42.9	48.4	54.2	60.7	67.5	74.1	81.4	89.1	96.5	104.3
Soil	59.5	66.3	73.7	81.5	89.5	97.8	105.7	114.5	122.9	131.4

Chapter 3
Reporting Your Data

Completing the Investigation

How to Interpret Your Data

After you complete your experiments, you will use the information (data) recorded in your journal to reach a conclusion. Do all of your data interpretation directly in your journal.

Possible ways to interpret your data in order to reach a conclusion include the following:

- Average the numbers.
- Compare beginning numbers to each other.
- Compare beginning numbers to final numbers.
- Compare final numbers to each other.
- Compare averages to each other.

Refer to the Sample Journal (pp. 49–52) to see how the data was interpreted in the ant investigation discussed in this book. Note that the figures have been adjusted to contain only significant figures. Refer to the following information about accuracy, precision, and significant figures.

Accuracy and Precision in Measurement

▣ Limitations of Measurement

Because scientific instruments are imperfect and people are fallible, measurements are never as certain as the physical world they attempt to describe. There are two kinds of certainty (or uncertainty) in scientific measurement: the **accuracy,** or exactness, of a measurement and the **precision,** or repeatability.

▣ *Accuracy* in Measurement

Measurements are not always exact. For example, you might step on a bathroom scale and see that you weigh 110 lb. You would know, however, that the scale does not provide an exact measurement of your weight; it gives you an *approximate* measurement. If you actually weighed 109.986158 lb, and your scale indicates that you weigh 110 lb, the measurement is off by 0.013842 lb.

Of course, a bathroom scale is accurate enough to fulfill its purpose; but a biologist seeking to weigh a gnat would find that a bathroom scale is not accurate enough for this measurement. To be **accurate** is to be exact instead of approximate; accuracy is concerned with *how closely a measurement or series of measurements reflects the actual value.*

▣ *Precision* in Measurement

Precision involves the *repeatability* of a measurement, or *how close several measurements of the same things are to each other.* If you weighed yourself on your bathroom scale 4 times in 4 minutes and it read 113 lb, 111 lb, 107 lb, and 109 lb, the scale was not very precise. The readings were reasonably accurate, but you could not say definitely that you weighed 110 lb; rather, you could say that you weighed between 107 and 113 lb, or that you weighed 110 lb plus or minus 3 lb. **Measurements must be consistent in order to be valid.** A more precise scale might have read

110.25 lb, 109.25 lb, 109.95 lb, and 109.80 lb, and a scientific scale might have read 110.001 lb, 110.015 lb, and 109.995 lb.

Accuracy and precision do not apply to numbers that can be counted exactly (you have 10 fingers) or numbers that are exact by definition (12 inches = 1 foot). These numbers are known as **exact numbers.**

▣ Significant Figures

Measurements that are not completely certain are generally handled in a special way, using what scientists call *significant figures.* **Significant figures** are a way to reflect the inaccuracies of a measurement when you record the final result. Some of the numbers in a measurement may be certain, but some probably are not. Scientists generally record measurements to the first uncertain digit. For example, when reading a measurement of 110.5 lb from the bathroom scale, there is some uncertainty in the last digit. The first three digits are certain, but you had to estimate that the pointer fell halfway between the 110 and 111 mark.

When you average the figures for your science project, take into account the number of significant figures. If each of your measurements has 4 significant figures, the average should include only 4 significant figures. For example, the average of 3 weighings on the bathroom scale (113.5 lb, 112.3 lb, and 109.5 lb) should be recorded as 111.8 lb instead of 111.76666667 lb).

Use the following guidelines to determine the number of significant figures:

1. Begin with the first non-zero digit and count the digits from left to right.
   2.000 (4 significant figures)
   .0002 (1 significant figure)

2. For whole numbers ending in zero and with no decimal point, do not count the ending zeros.

15,000 (2 significant figures)

15,000. (5 significant figures)

3. When operating with measured values, the answer is only as accurate as the measurement with the greatest uncertainty.

Remember, your results are only as accurate as your least accurate measurement.

How to Graph Your Data

The next step in interpreting your data is to convert it into graphs. Graphs illustrate data in an easy-to-understand format. Keep your graphs simple and accurate.

▣ *What kinds of graphs should I use?*

The most helpful types of graphs are **bar** and **line graphs.** Bar graphs are useful for comparing results of several experiments or experimental groups at a *single point in time.* Line graphs are useful for showing the *progression* of an individual experiment or experimental group over a period of time.

▣ *What are some characteristics of good graphs?*

Good graphs...

1. are large enough to be clearly seen.

2. clearly show the differences (by color or other methods) among items being graphed together.

3. are quickly and easily understood.

4. include a key to explain colors or symbols used.

5. have a title that tells their purpose.

6. have labels for each axis to indicate what it represents and what measuring units it uses (meters, minutes, etc.).

Your completed graphs will be included in your Investigation Followup. Remember to double-check all mathematical calculations.

Types of Graphs

Bar Graphs

A **bar graph** is a graph that uses horizontal or vertical bars (column graph) to illustrate data. Bar graphs are good for showing frequency (how often something occurred) and overall average results. The quantities represented in the graph can be easily compared by examining the length of the bars.

To construct a bar graph, use the following steps:

1. Decide upon a scale using appropriate numbers of convenient size. The highest axis point on your graph should be slightly larger than your highest measurement. For example, if the highest number in your data is fifteen,

then your highest axis point may be twenty with intervals of two and a half.

2. Label what each bar represents.

3. Write the title above the bar graph.

4. Include the values for each bar.

Example:

A horizontal bar graph might be constructed to illustrate the following information about the average hourly speed of Western harvester ants that tunnel in an artificial habitat (gel) versus the same ants in their natural habitat (soil): Ants tunneling in an artificial habitat tunnel at 0.2 cm per hour; ants in a natural habitat tunnel at 0.3 cm per hour.

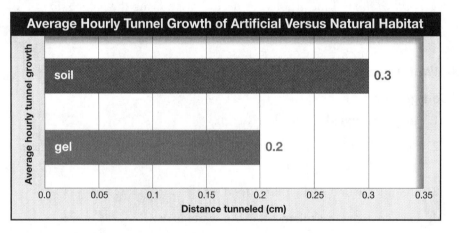

The same information used to construct the horizontal bar graph might be used to make a vertical graph. Notice that in the sample below, the scale numbers are placed at the left of the lines.

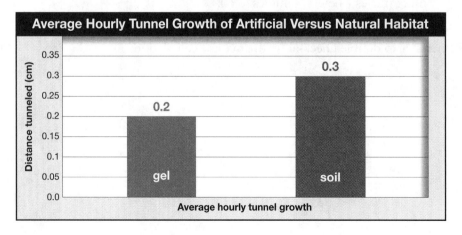

Line Graphs

Line graphs are used to record and plot numerical data such as lengths, temperatures, etc. Usually the data on a line graph are closely related and show how the data changed over a period of time. Most spreadsheet programs will assign a legend to the graph; be sure to enter appropriate labels for your legend.

When you make your line graph, have the x-axis (horizontal axis) represent your intervals of time. These periods of time should be of equal length—days, weeks, etc.—not variable—such as day 1, day 5, day 6, etc. The y-axis (vertical axis) represents what you are measuring (your variable).

Example:

In the experiment to determine the cumulative daily tunnel growth of each ant group (gel versus soil), the cumulative tunnel growth was calculated in centimeters and plotted on a line graph.

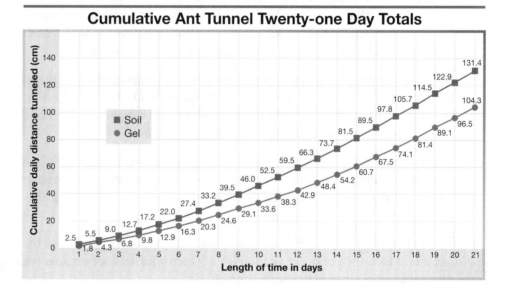

How to Form a Conclusion

The conclusion you reach for your Investigation will become part of your Followup report and will be included as a separate section of your exhibit display. To form a conclusion, consider your hypothesis and study your graphs (data) to determine what your investigation has shown.

Step 1: Consider Your Hypothesis. As you form a conclusion, you will be answering the question, "Do these results support my hypothesis?" Do not be concerned if your hypothesis seems to be incorrect. Every scientist has made an incorrect hypothesis. If your results do not support your hypothesis, look through your journal for some explanation as to why this occurred.

Step 2: Study Your Graphs. Your graphs will help you form a conclusion because they show the relationship between your variable and your results.

The Investigation Followup is a written report that briefly describes your experiments, results, and conclusion.

Guidelines for Writing the Followup

▣ *What should my Investigation Followup include?*

The Investigation Followup has three sections. Write a clear description for each of the following:

1. **Procedure**—a paragraph that reviews briefly what your investigation involved. Mention your sample size and/or how many repetitions you used. Include your variable and control. State whether you were able to follow your Investigation Plan; if you made any changes, describe them.

2. **Results/Graphs**—a statement of the outcome of the investigation. Include mathematical statistics. Example: "The plants in Group B reached an average height of 14.0 cm." These results should be supported by graphs. All measurements should be expressed in metric units.

3. **Conclusion**—a statement of the conclusion you reached based on the outcome of your investigation. Indicate whether your conclusion supported your hypothesis and why or why not. End the conclusion by stating practical benefits that you have learned from your investigation.

After you have written your Followup first draft and revised it, complete the final draft and attach the Followup Grade Form. Once your teacher returns your paper, place it in your Science Project Notebook.

INVESTIGATION FOLLOWUP

YOUR NAME
DATE
TEACHER'S NAME
CLASS

Investigation Followup

PROCEDURE

My investigation was to make a comparison of how a certain species of ant tunnels in an artificial environment compared to a natural environment. The problem was, "Do Western harvester ants dig tunnels at a different rate in an artificial environment compared to the same ants that dig tunnels in their natural habitat?" A second question was, "Is the width of the tunnels of Western harvester ants affected when they are placed in an artificial environment?" My hypothesis was that ants will not tunnel in the artificial environment as quickly as in a natural habitat and that the width of their tunnels would not be affected by living in the artificial environment.

To begin this experiment, I purchased two plastic formicariums from a science supply company. The dimensions of both formicariums were 16.5 centimeters in length, 2.5 centimeters in width, and 7.5 centimeters in depth. Unlike a normal ant farm, the artificial soil formicarium contained a gel that was developed for use in space shuttle experiments. I filled the empty formicarium with sandy soil (the natural habitat of the ants). Finally, I purchased apples to use as food, and I obtained an eyedropper to give water to the ants.

1

2

After I received the formicariums, I received the shipment
of Western harvester ants. In order to transfer them from
the plastic container to the formicarium, I had to place the
container in the refrigerator for ten minutes until the ants
slowed down enough so that I could transfer them safely. I wore
gloves and handled them with forceps. I moved twenty-five ants
to each formicarium and covered each container. These were all
worker ants; there was not a queen.

Every eight hours, I observed the formicariums to see if
the ants had begun to tunnel. Once they had, I measured in
centimeters how far they had tunneled. I placed adhesive notes
on the formicariums to indicate where the ants started and
stopped tunneling. I also measured the width of the tunnels and
recorded my observations of the ants' behavior.

There was no control group in my experiment. The constants
in my experiment were the type of ants, the width of the starter
holes, the location of the formicariums, the size of the
formicariums, and the amounts of food and water I gave to each
colony. Every eight hours, I took measurements of the increase
in tunnel length and diameter and determined the average number
of tunnels that were dug each hour. After each measurement,
I recorded the cumulative total tunnel length and made a line

graph of the results. I also recorded the average hourly and daily tunnel growth and put this information on a bar graph. I carried out the experiments over a twenty-one-day period.

RESULTS

The ants in each formicarium began digging their first tunnel after approximately eight hours. In the gel (artificial environment), approximately eight ants began digging the first tunnel and worked at an average rate of 0.2 centimeters per hour. After the fourth day, there was a noticeable increase in the number of ants that helped to tunnel. The ants in the artificial environment tunneled only 1.8 cm in the first twenty-four hours (see graph 1). Each day thereafter, the amount of tunneling increased for a cumulative total over the twenty-one-day period

Graph 1

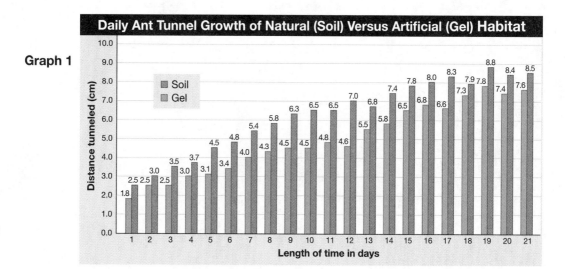

of 104.3 cm (see graph 4). There were three days where there was

a decrease in the length of the tunnel compared to what the ants

had dug the previous day. The average hourly tunneling speed

over the twenty-one-day period was 0.2 cm (see graph 2). The

average tunneling per day over the twenty-one-day period was 5 cm

(see graph 3).

Ants in the natural habitat tunneled 2.5 cm after the first

24 hrs (see graph 1). These ants tunneled at an average rate of

Graph 2

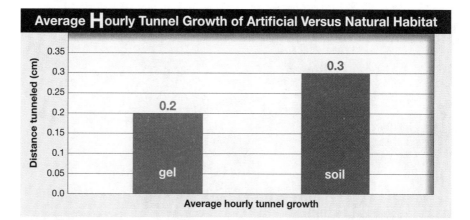

Graph 3

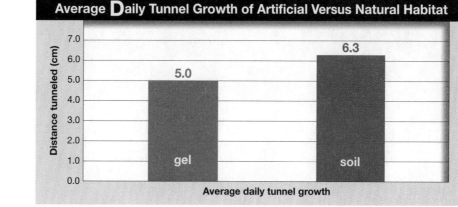

0.3 cm per hour (see graph 2). The average tunneling per day over the twenty-one-day period was 6.3 cm (see graph 3). The ants in the natural habitat tunneled for an average of 1.3 cm longer per day than the ants in the gel. The hourly tunnel growth of the ants in the natural habitat was also longer by an average of 0.1 cm.

The day with the greatest amount of tunneling was day twenty-one, where the ants in the soil tunneled 9 cm and the ants in the artificial environment tunneled 9 cm. There were four days where there was a decrease in the length of the tunnel compared to what the ants had dug the previous day. The cumulative tunneling total for the ants in the natural habitat was 131.4 cm (see graph 4). I did not record observations after day twenty-one. The ants in both habitats were only able to tunnel to a

Graph 4

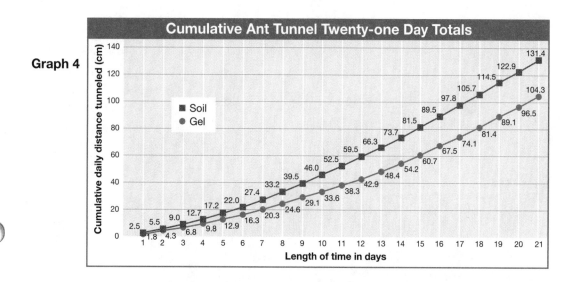

depth of 7.5 cm because that was the depth of the gel and soil. The average width of the tunneling was 1 cm for each colony of ants.

CONCLUSION

From the data I gathered, my hypothesis was correct in that the Western harvester ants tunneled at a quicker rate in their natural habitat than in an artificial environment. After twenty-one days of tunneling in the artificial environment of gel, the average hourly tunnel growth was 0.2 cm, and it was 0.3 cm in the natural habitat (see graph 2). For the first four days of observation, only eight ants were regularly working on the tunneling in the soil. That may be a reason why they only averaged approximately 3.2 cm for the first four days (see graph 1). Not until fifteen ants were regularly working on tunneling did the daily average length of the tunnels began to increase. On day five, the tunneling in the soil for that day increased to 4.5 cm. For my second problem that had to do with the width of each tunnel, the ants in each habitat averaged one centimeter for each tunnel so there was no distinguishable difference.

Chapter 4
Preparing Your Exhibit

Now that your investigation is complete, it is time to plan and build your Science Project Exhibit. The exhibit includes your Science Project Notebook, your display board, and any models or equipment that help explain your project.

Project Notebook

What's Included in the Notebook?

1. Background paper
2. Investigation Plan
3. Followup
4. Journal
5. Worksheets

How Do I Set Up My Notebook?

1. Prepare a title page.

    a. Center the title, SCIENCE PROJECT NOTEBOOK, two inches from the top of the page (between margins), using all capitals.

    b. Type the following information two inches from the bottom in the center: name, date, teacher's name, and class using all capitals.

2. Insert the Background paper, Investigation Plan, and Followup in that order.

3. Insert the Journal after preparing a title page with the title "JOURNAL" centered two inches from the top of the page.

    Note: Names of people tested in your investigation should not appear anywhere in your Journal or Notebook.

4. Insert worksheets after preparing a title page with the title "WORKSHEETS" centered two inches from the top of the page.

Guidelines for Displaying the Project

◉ **What information should go on the display board?**

Your display board should contain a brief summary of each area of your investigation. Since your investigation is complete, you should write everything in the past tense, using correct scientific terms. All measurements should be in metric units. If people were tested in the investigation, their names and/or photos should not appear anywhere on the display.

Include the following information on the display board:

1. **Title**—an interesting title that is two or more words. The following are some examples:

   Snail Trails

   Fingerprints: The Invisible Signature

   Does Microwave Radiation Affect Seed Germination?

   The Effect of Pheromones on Ant Behavior

2. **Problem**—a statement of the question/problem you have investigated

3. **Hypothesis**—what you believed the answer to your question/problem to be before you began the investigation

4. **Variable**—the one factor or condition that was present only in the experimental group

5. **Procedure**—a list of numbered steps of how you performed your investigation. Illustrate the steps with as many drawings or photos as possible.

6. **Results**—a statement of the outcome supported by graphs

7. **Conclusion**—the conclusion you reached accompanied by an explanation of whether it supported your hypothesis or not. State the practical benefits learned.

◉ **How should the information be displayed?**

1. All lettering should be neat and readable. Title letters should be at least 3" tall and subtitles (for Problem, Hypothesis, etc.) should be at least 1" tall.

2. Type all display information in a type size (16–18 pt.) that can be easily read 3–5 feet away from the board. For longer printed sections such as Procedure, it may be necessary to mount typed sheets on top of each other. Staple them at the top so that the first sheet can be lifted to read the second sheet, etc.

3. Use a ruler to make sure that all items on your board are mounted straight.

◉ **What other items can be displayed with the board?**

1. Display basic equipment and supplies used in the investigation.

2. Do not display chemicals, bacteria and fungi cultures, or other potentially harmful substances.

Remember that the first impression that others will form of your investigation is by what they see. A sharp display creates an excellent first impression.

◉ **Where will I show my exhibit?**

You will use the exhibit to present the project to your class during your oral presentation. Your teacher may also ask you to display your exhibit at a school science fair and/or a regional science fair.

If you have several experiments, describe the hypothesis, variable, procedure, results, and conclusion for **each** one. The diagram on the next page shows one suggested organization of items on your display board.

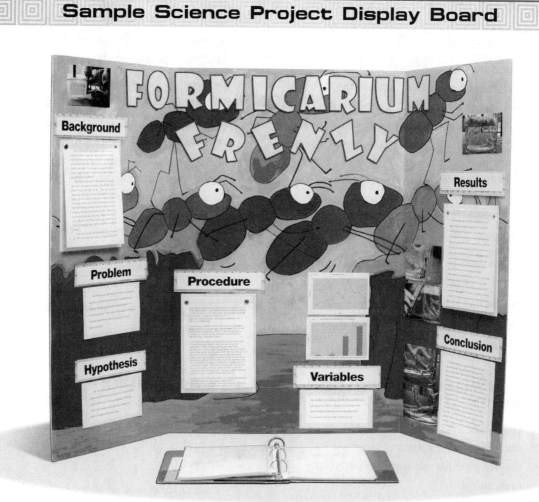

Presenting Your Science Project

The purpose of your presentation is to tell your class the story of your investigation in a clear, interesting way. Your exhibit is an important visual aid in your presentation. You will refer to it often as you explain your project.

Guidelines for Giving the Oral Presentation

Your presentation should include the following sections:

1. **Introduction**—an interesting *opening statement* to catch everyone's attention, followed by an *explanation of the topic*. Your explanation should introduce your topic and give basic information about it. This part of the presentation is actually a miniature lesson in which you *teach* the class about your topic. Include enough general information from your Background paper to set the stage for the explanation of your investigation.

2. **Problem/Hypothesis**—an explanation of the *problem* you investigated and your *hypothesis*

3. **Procedure**—an explanation of the *steps you followed* to complete the investigation, including a description of the *variable, constant factors,* and *control* (if applicable). If possible, *demonstrate* the steps and *show* the equipment you used. Include any interesting things that occurred during your investigation. Tell how you overcame problems which arose.

4. **Results**—an explanation of the *outcome* of the investigation and how you *graphed* the results on the board

5. **Conclusion**—an explanation of the *conclusion* you reached based on the results shown in your graphs. Include whether your results support your *hypothesis* and why. Mention *practical applications* for this investigation.

How long should my presentation be?

The oral presentation has a minimum and maximum time requirement. The time allowed for questioning by your audience is not counted as part of your time requirement.

Suggested Time
(in Minutes)

Grade	Minimum	Maximum
8	4	6
9	5	7
10	6	8
11	7	9

Preparing for the Oral Presentation

Step 1: Organize your thoughts, deciding what facts and information you should give for each section of your presentation.

Step 2: Since you will not be reading your presentation, prepare **note cards** to refer to as you speak.

Step 3: Practice your presentation at least **three** times. Have someone watch your presentation and give suggestions. Be positive about your investigation, even if you did not enjoy it.

How can I make my presentation effective?

1. Speak freely without being tied to notes.

2. Make eye contact with the audience.

3. Show equipment items by holding them up and pointing to key parts so that all can see.

4. Stand at the side of the display while referring to graphs and other exhibit items. Do not turn your back to the class or stand in front of your exhibit.

5. Be ready to answer questions from your classmates and teacher.

What do I need on the day of my presentation?

1. Notecards

2. Exhibit (display board, notebook, models and/or equipment)

3. Grade form

Appendix

In your Background paper, you are not expected to come up with and discuss original ideas. Your task is to collect and organize information from **several** sources. While general scientific knowledge does not need to be documented, you should give credit to any source from which you take an author's exact words, original ideas, or opinions.

To document information, use the parenthetical citation format. See *Handbook of Grammar & Composition (A Beka Book)* for a fuller explanation of parenthetical citations.

Procedures for Parenthetical Notes

1. Each time you need to give credit to an author, cite in parentheses the author and page number. If the author's name is used in your sentence, then provide only the page number in the parentheses. Since Internet sources generally do not have page numbers, use just the author's name in the citation. (See sample below.)

2. Since the Background paper is not a formal research paper, place a bibliography entry for each cited source below the last paragraph of the paper. Alphabetize the bibliography entries by the first word of the entry (generally the author's last name). Do not use a title before the bibliography entries. (See sample below for formatting.)

Sample

Observations of the one-foot and two-foot model boats proved my hypothesis that length, speed, and weight together affect the wave patterns produced by ships. According to Edward Lewis and Robert O'Brien, the British engineer William Froude used larger models to discover the same fact: the wave pattern caused by the hull of a small ship moving slowly through the water is proportionally the same as the wave pattern caused by the hull of a larger ship moving faster (34). Froude went on to conclude that two hulls of the same shape traveling at similar speeds encounter resistance in direct proportion to displacement, or the total weight of the ship and its cargo (Lewis and O'Brien, 33). It can therefore be concluded that it is not only the length and speed of the ship that changes the wave pattern, but also the weight or displacement.

← Citation with authors named in text

← Citation with authors' names and page number

I also found that as the model's speed increases, fewer transverse waves are formed, but they are much larger. A report by nautical designer John Winters confirmed this finding (Winters).

← Internet citation

Lewis, Edward, and Robert O'Brien. *Ships*. New York: Time-Life Books, 1970.

Winters, John. "The Shape of the Canoe." http://greenval.com/shape-part2 .html (accessed June 18, 2011).

Format for
Parenthetical Citations and Bibliographies

In the following examples, **"PC"** indicates a parenthetical citation, and **"B"** indicates a bibliographical entry.

Book with one author

PC (Hughes, 127)

B Hughes, Jonathan. *American Economic History.* Glenview, Ill.: Scott Foresman, 1983.

(List author, title of book, city of publication, publisher, most recent publication date.)

Book with two authors

PC (Hoebel and Frost, 325–326)

B Hoebel, E. Adamson, and Everett L. Frost. *Cultural and Social Anthropology.* New York: McGraw-Hill Co., 1976.

(List authors, title of book, city of publication, publisher, most recent publication date.)

Encyclopedia

PC *(The World Book Encyclopedia)*

B *The World Book Encyclopedia,* 1992 ed. S.v. "Nuclear energy" by Vera Kistiakowksy.

(List title of encyclopedia, edition date, "S.v.," name of article, and author of article. For unsigned articles, omit author's name.)

General Magazine

PC (Gilder, 23)

B Gilder, George. "What Ronald Reagan Doesn't Know about His Own Achievements." *National Review,* June 29, 1984, 22–25.

(List author, title of article, title of journal, date, page number.)

Professional Journal

PC (Shields, 545)

B Shields, David S. "Happiness in Society: The Development of an Eighteenth-Century American Poetic Ideal." *American Literature* 55 (December 1983): 541–559.

(List author's name, title of article, title of journal, volume number, date, page number.)

World Wide Web (WWW) page

PC (Simanek)

(For unsigned articles, use title of Web page in place of author's name.)

B Simanek, Donald E. "Nature's Impossibilities." 2008. http://lhup .ed/~dsimanek/museum/impossible.htm (accessed April 28, 2011).

(List author's name, title of article, date, Internet address [URL], and accessed date. For unsigned articles, omit author's name and begin with title of article.)

MECHANICS. . . . . 10 points _____

    Following Directions

    Punctuation and Capitalization

    Grammar and Spelling

    Sentence and Paragraph Structure

CONTENT . . . . 90 points _____

    Organization

    Length

    Presentation of Topic (clarity, unity, coherence, emphasis)

Total points _____

(counts as one quiz)

Teacher Investigation Plan Evaluation

Your teacher evaluated your plan and made recommendations on this form.

Problem or Question

- ☐ State a separate problem for each experiment.
- ☐ Restate using more specific wording.
- ☐ No change needed.

Hypothesis

- ☐ State a reason for the hypothesis that you chose.
- ☐ State a separate hypothesis for each experiment.
- ☐ Restate your hypothesis to reflect what you have learned in your research.
- ☐ Restate your hypothesis using more specific wording.
- ☐ No change needed.

Procedure

Experimental Design

- ☐ State the number of separate experiments you will be doing.
- ☐ Describe the specific steps of each of your experiments in detail.
- ☐ Describe the following specific area in more detail:

  _____

- ☐ For each of your experiments, describe or clarify the following:
  - ☐ experimental group
  - ☐ control (if needed)
  - ☐ constant factors
  - ☐ variable
  - ☐ number of trials
- ☐ No change needed.

Measurement Technique

- ☐ Describe the specific way you will measure the result of each experiment, including the tools, instruments, and units of measure you will use (always use metric units).
- ☐ Describe the method of graphing the results for each experiment including the type of data to be plotted on each axis.
- ☐ State the sources of published data with which to compare your results (if applicable).

Extensiveness

☐ Increase the number of trials.

☐ Increase the number of experiments to at least _____.

☐ Enlarge the experimental group to at least _____ members.

☐ No change needed.

Conclusion

☐ State the standard (measurement change) that you will use to decide if your hypothesis is correct.

☐ Restate your standard (measurement change) so that it is reasonable.

☐ Clearly state how you will determine whether your hypothesis was proven correct or incorrect.

☐ No change needed.

Safety

☐ Include safety procedures regarding _____.

☐ Restate your safety procedures using more specific wording.

☐ No change needed.

Other Considerations

Journal Observations

☐ Describe the types of observations (color changes, movements, etc.) that you will record in your journal for each experiment.

Teacher Investigation Plan Evaluation

Your teacher evaluated your plan and made recommendations on this form.

Problem or Question

☐ State a separate problem for each experiment.

☐ Restate using more specific wording.

☐ No change needed.

Hypothesis

☐ State a reason for the hypothesis that you chose.

☐ State a separate hypothesis for each experiment.

☐ Restate your hypothesis to reflect what you have learned in your research.

☐ Restate your hypothesis using more specific wording.

☐ No change needed.

Procedure

Experimental Design

☐ State the number of separate experiments you will be doing.

☐ Describe the specific steps of each of your experiments in detail.

☐ Describe the following specific area in more detail:

_____

☐ For each of your experiments, describe or clarify the following:

    ☐ experimental group

    ☐ control (if needed)

    ☐ constant factors

    ☐ variable

    ☐ number of trials

☐ No change needed.

Measurement Technique

☐ Describe the specific way you will measure the result of each experiment, including the tools, instruments, and units of measure you will use (always use metric units).

☐ Describe the method of graphing the results for each experiment including the type of data to be plotted on each axis.

☐ State the sources of published data with which to compare your results (if applicable).

Extensiveness

☐ Increase the number of trials.

☐ Increase the number of experiments to at least _____.

☐ Enlarge the experimental group to at least _____ members.

☐ No change needed.

Conclusion

☐ State the standard (measurement change) that you will use to decide if your hypothesis is correct.

☐ Restate your standard (measurement change) so that it is reasonable.

☐ Clearly state how you will determine whether your hypothesis was proven correct or incorrect.

☐ No change needed.

Safety

☐ Include safety procedures regarding _____.

☐ Restate your safety procedures using more specific wording.

☐ No change needed.

Other Considerations

Journal Observations

☐ Describe the types of observations (color changes, movements, etc.) that you will record in your journal for each experiment.

Investigation Plan Grade Form

MECHANICS

Neatness, Following Directions, Punctuation and Capitalization,
Grammar and Spelling, Sentence and Paragraph Structure .... 30 points _____

EXPERIMENTAL DESIGN

Problem—Legitimate, specific problem clearly stated .... 10 points _____

Hypothesis—Sound hypothesis clearly stated .... 10 points _____

PROCEDURE

Level of Complexity .... 10 points _____

Procedure Clearly Described—Details are understandable. .... 8 points _____

Clear Variable—Everything else held constant .... 7 points _____

Control Explained .... 4 points _____

Sample Size/Number of Experiments—Adequate number to reach
a valid conclusion .... 7 points _____

Number of Trials—Adequate number to reach a valid conclusion .... 7 points _____

Accuracy of Measurement Technique—Measurement is accurate
to ensure a valid conclusion. .... 7 points _____

Total points _____

(counts as two quizzes)

Followup Grade Form

FORMAT (Neatness, Following Directions) . . . . 10 points _____

CONTENT (30 points each) . . . . 90 points _____

    Procedure, Results/Graphs, Conclusion

Total points _____

(counts as one quiz)

Science Project Final Grade Form

Name _____

Title _____

Problem Statement(s) _____

_____

Oral Presentation Criteria

I. Delivery/Content .... 20 points

Consider the following:

- **Gave effective presentation**—posture, gestures, eye contact, vocal quality, interesting
- Delivered presentation **without relying too heavily on notes**
- Kept presentation **within the time range** assigned

| 8th grade (4–6 min.) | 10th grade (6–8 min.) |
| 9th grade (5–7 min.) | 11th grade (7–9 min.) |

Evaluate the oral presentation for adequate explanation of background, problem, hypothesis, variable, results, data, and conclusion.

Comments: _____

_____

_____

Total points Section I: _____

II. Experimental Design of Project .... 50 points

Consider the following:

- Constitutes **legitimate scientific investigation** (rather than a demonstration or model)
- Adheres to **investigation plan** (creative improvements are fine)
- Investigates a **specific problem** and offers a **sound hypothesis** regarding the solution
- Employs **controlled experiment(s)** having one variable and other factors held constant
- Reflects adequate **level of difficulty**
- Includes sufficient **sample size** and **number of experiments** or trials
- Applies **accurate measurement techniques** (reflected in journal) to ensure a valid conclusion

Comments: _____

_____

_____

Total points Section II: _____

Exhibit Criteria

III. Design of Display / Content / Notebook

Consider the following concerning

the student's exhibit board: .... 20 points _____

- Interesting and informative **title**
- Good **color** combination
- **Creative** display of information
- Straight, **neat,** logical arrangement
- **Pictures** or **drawings** that illustrate the topic/procedures; equipment/materials displayed if possible
- Type size and style that is **easily read**
- Clear, accurate **charts** and **graphs,** each titled and labeled

Check the display board for clear,

logical statements of the following: .... 8 points _____

- Background
- Problem
- Hypothesis
- Procedure
- Variable
- Results
- Conclusion

Consider the following concerning

the student's notebook: .... 2 points _____

- All the parts are included.
- The student has followed directions.

Comments: _____

_____

_____

_____

_____

Total points Section III: _____

Points for Section I: _____

Points for Section II: + _____

Points for Section III: + _____

FINAL GRADE: _____

(counts as one test)

Approved for Science Fair: _____

Science Project Judging Form

DIVISION _____   CATEGORY _____

DATE _____   EXHIBIT NUMBER _____   JUDGE _____

Exhibit

	Poor	Fair	Good	Excellent	Points
Title	**0 pts.** Title is boring and does not apply to project.	**1 pt.** Title applies to project but is boring.	**3 pts.** Title is creative and applies to project.	**5 pts.** Title is creative, attention-getting, and applicable to project.	_____
Board	**0–4 pts.** Board is boring, and it does not relate to project.	**5–8 pts.** Board is boring, but it adequately supports the project.	**9–12 pts.** Board is creative or colorful. It supports the project.	**13–15 pts.** Board is creative and colorful. It draws attention while supporting the project.	_____
Posted material	**0–2 pts.** Material is readable and provides some information about the project.	**3–5 pts.** Material is readable and generally tells the project's story.	**6–8 pts.** Material is orderly, readable, and generally tells the project's story.	**9–10 pts.** Material is orderly, readable, and clearly tells the project's story.	_____
Graphs	**0 pts.** Graphs have little to no relation to data or project.	**1 pt.** Graphs are readable but are missing parts.	**3 pts.** Graphs are readable and include titles, legends, and scales.	**5 pts.** Graphs are readable and helpful, including titles, legends, and scales.	_____
Journal	**0 pts.** No journal entries are provided.	**1 pt.** Journal is messy and is missing information.	**3 pts.** Journal is messy, or it is missing data or project information.	**5 pts.** Journal is neatly written and provides useful data and project information.	_____

(40 points maximum) **Total points** [ ]

Scientific Process

	Poor	Fair	Good	Excellent	Points
Problems	**0–2 pts.** Problems are not clear.	**3–5 pts.** Problems are clearly stated and have obvious answers but are not thoughtful.	**6–8 pts.** Problems are clearly stated and thoughtful but have obvious answers.	**9–10 pts.** Problems are clearly stated and are thoughtful, without obvious answers.	_____
Hypotheses	**0–2 pts.** Hypotheses are guesses.	**3–5 pts.** Hypotheses are accurate but do not show sound reasoning.	**6–8 pts.** Hypotheses show sound reasoning but are not accurate.	**9–10 pts.** Hypotheses show accurate and sound reasoning, not guessing.	_____
Procedure	**0–4 pts.** Procedure is complete but not easy to follow and does not show scientific thinking or creativity.	**5–8 pts.** Procedure is complete and easy to follow but does not show scientific thinking or creativity.	**9–12 pts.** Procedure is complete, easy to follow, and shows scientific thinking. It does not show creativity.	**13–15 pts.** Procedure is complete, easy to follow, and shows scientific thinking and creativity.	_____
Experiments	**0–2 pts.** Experiment does not answer obvious questions. Trials and sample sizes are not adequate.	**3–5 pts.** Experiment answers obvious questions. Trials and sample sizes are not adequate.	**6–8 pts.** Experiment answers obvious questions and has adequate trials. Sample sizes are not adequate.	**9–10 pts.** Experiment answers obvious questions and has adequate trials and sample sizes.	_____
Variables	**0 pts.** Variables are not at all consistent with Problems or Procedure.	**1 pt.** Variables are consistent with Procedure but not with Problems.	**3 pts.** Variables are consistent with Problems but not with Procedure.	**5 pts.** Variables are consistent with Problems and Procedure.	_____
Results	**0 pts.** Results seem fictional.	**1 pt.** Results are unlikely and are not consistent with Procedure and Variables.	**3 pts.** Results are unlikely but are consistent with Procedure.	**5 pts.** Results are valid and are consistent with Procedure and Variables.	_____
Conclusion	**0 pts.** Conclusion is inconsistent and incomplete.	**1 pt.** Conclusion is consistent with Results but is incomplete.	**3 pts.** Conclusion is consistent with Procedure and Results but is incomplete.	**5 pts.** Conclusion is valid, is consistent with Procedure and Results, and shows sound reasoning.	_____

(60 points maximum) **Total points** [ ]

Grand total [ ]
(100 points maximum)